The Best Of
Alex
2008

Charles Peattie & Russell Taylor

Masterley Publishing

The Best Of
Alex
2008

First Published in 2008 by MASTERLEY PUBLISHING

Layout and Artwork: Suzette Field

ISBN: 978-1-84222-792-3

Printed in the UK by CPI William Clowes Beccles NR34 7TL

Our usual gratitude goes to our generous sponsors:

FTSE Group - provider of global equity, fixed income, alternative asset class, responsible investment & investment strategy indices; and Mondo Visione - the leading source of insight and knowledge about the world's exchanges and trading venues.

FOREWORD

At the time of writing Alex was about to experience the third recession of his career. Naturally he did not see it coming. Prior to August 2007 (where this book opens) hardly anyone in the City had heard of sub-prime debt – even though their banks' wealth was founded on it and had indeed already been substantially undermined by it. Yet by September depositors were queuing to get their money out of Northern Rock, giving the expression "a run on a bank" a meaning other than one's lunchtime training jog along the Thames.

As commentators on the business world we are of course always deeply grateful when the highly-paid people we write about cock up quite so monumentally and provide us with months of free material at their own expense. We join the rest of the population in laughing with a certain schadenfreude at the City's stupidity in piling blindly into a market that they just naively assumed would continue to go up forever. Then we remember how much we paid for that house we so rashly mortgaged ourselves up to the hilt to buy last year.. and what it's worth today.

Ah yes, that's the problem: the short termism and greed of people like Alex can easily engender a recession, but it's the rest of us who have to pick up the pieces. And, unlike the City guys whose fault it all was, we haven't salted away years' worth of colossal bonuses that we made on the upside.

Despite this, the popular perception is that economic downturns are actually quite convenient for us financial satirists. People ask us - with the confident smile of someone who thinks they already know the answer to their question - whether we will just be recycling all our old recession jokes from the last time round.

Well, it's a tempting idea, but we'd be very unlikely to get away with it. Our readers are eagle-eyed in picking us up on mistakes and inconsistencies in the strip. For example if we misposition the flower arrangement in a first class aircraft cabin or the lifebelt on a Sunseeker yacht our inbox will be full of emails pointing out our error (though perhaps this will be less prevalent now that our readers are having to sell their yachts on eBay and fly at the back of the plane).

So no, despite having produced over 5000 Alex strips (strip number 5000 is at the bottom of page 46 if you're interested), we would no more dream of consciously repeating ourselves than the financial community would. Sub-prime mortgages, anyone? Dotcom start-ups? South Sea Company stock? Tulip bulbs?

Charles Peattie and Russell Taylor

Penny - Alex's wife

Clive - Alex's colleague

Bridget - Clive's wife

Alex

Rupert - senior banker

Cyrus - Alex's boss

Christopher - Alex's son

Carolyn - Alex's mistress

Hardcastle - Alex's client

Fabergé - lapdancer

Christian - Euro-banker

11

Alex PEATTIE + TAYLOR

I THINK CHRISTOPHER IS RELIEVED THAT HIS SUMMER INTERNSHIP IN THE CITY IS FINALLY OVER...

I CAN IMAGINE WHY...

I MEAN, WHEN I WAS HIS AGE WE DIDN'T BOTHER WITH GETTING WORK EXPERIENCE...I'D SPEND MY LONG HOLIDAYS PLAYING CRICKET OR GOING CAMPING WITH MY FRIENDS OR JUST HANGING OUT

YES...

IT MUST BE VERY FRUSTRATING FOR KIDS NOWADAYS HAVING TO SPEND THEIR SUMMER SITTING AT A DESK IN AN OPPRESSIVE OFFICE ENVIRONMENT AND BEING DENIED THE NATURAL SOCIAL INTERACTION WITH THEIR PEER GROUP...

THAT'S TRUE...

"FACEBOOK" IS BANNED IN ALL BANKS THESE DAYS.

HE HASN'T MOVED FROM THE COMPUTER IN HIS BEDROOM SINCE HE GOT BACK TWO DAYS AGO...

Alex PEATTIE + TAYLOR

HOW COME NONE OF THE BOSSES ARE AROUND THIS WEEK?

BECAUSE NOW EVERYONE'S BACK FROM THEIR HOLIDAYS, IT'S THE CONFERENCE SEASON...

AND ALL THE BANK'S SENIOR DIRECTORS HAVE FLOWN OFF SOMEWHERE AGREEABLE TO DISCUSS WAYS OF IMPROVING THE BANK'S EFFICIENCY AND PROFITABILITY...

HA! WELL THEY COULD START BY BANNING THIS SORT OF JUNKET...

THAT'S UNFAIR, CLIVE... A HIGH-LEVEL DISCUSSION OF THE BANK'S TOP BODS CAN BE A VERY EFFICIENT WAY OF IDENTIFYING AND ADDRESSING CORE PROBLEMS IN THE BANK'S BUSINESS...

ITEM 3 ON THEIR AGENDA IS: WHAT TO DO ABOUT THE UNFEASIBLE AMOUNT OF INTERNAL E-MAIL EVERYONE GETS THESE DAYS...

YES. HAS ANYONE ELSE NOTICED THAT THERE'S BEEN HARDLY ANY OF IT SINCE THEY'VE BEEN AWAY?

Alex PEATTIE + TAYLOR

SO, NICK, HOW WAS YOUR SABBATICAL?

MARVELLOUS, THANKS, ALEX. MY COMPANY GAVE ME 3 MONTHS OFF...

AND AFTER TWENTY YEARS IN THE CITY I FELT I HAD A WELL-EARNED BREAK COMING TO ME, SO I TREATED MYSELF TO A RELAXING SUMMER OF TRAVEL, WATCHING SPORT AND GENERAL SELF-INDULGENCE...

BUT ONE CAN'T DO THAT SORT OF THING FOR EVER, ALEX AND THERE COMES A TIME WHEN ONE'S GOT TO GET BACK TO THE SERIOUS WORLD OF BUSINESS...

OF COURSE...

THE RUGBY WORLD CUP'S STARTED AND YOU WOULDN'T WANT TO HAVE TO PAY FOR THAT OUT OF YOUR OWN POCKET.

QUITE. I'VE JUST GOT MY CORPORATE INVITE TO MARSEILLE FOR THE QUARTER FINALS...

Alex PEATTIE + TAYLOR

THE HOST NATION FRANCE HAS MADE A POOR START TO THE RUGBY WORLD CUP...

THERE'S NOW A DANGER THAT THEY MIGHT NOT QUALIFY FOR THE KNOCKOUT STAGES OF THE TOURNAMENT, WHICH WOULD OBVIOUSLY BE A MASSIVE BLOW TO GALLIC PRIDE...

YES, THEY'D FIND THE HUMILIATION TOTALLY UNBEARABLE...

WELL, THERE'S NO LOVE LOST BETWEEN THE ENGLISH AND THE FRENCH AT THE BEST OF TIMES AND THIS TURN OF EVENTS HAS HAD A PREDICTABLE EFFECT ON ALEX'S TREATMENT OF OUR PARISIAN JUNIOR, CHRISTIAN...

YES.

HE'S SUDDENLY BEING AMAZINGLY SYCOPHANTIC TOWARDS HIM...

CHRISTIAN'S DAD'S GOT A BOX AT THE STADE DE FRANCE AND AT THIS RATE THERE COULD BE A FEW EMPTY PLACES IN IT FOR THE FINAL...

CAN I GET YOU A COFFEE, CHRISTIAN?

14

Alex PEATTIE + TAYLOR

THERE'S A GREEN REVOLUTION GOING ON IN THIS COUNTRY AND NOT JUST IN THE HUGE RISE IN SALES OF ORGANIC FOOD...

MORE AND MORE PEOPLE ARE PUTTING WIND TURBINES ON THE ROOFS OF THEIR HOUSES... BUT THAT'S JUST A GESTURE OF ENVIRONMENTAL TOKENISM, PENNY. I CAN'T IMAGINE THEY GENERATE MUCH POWER...

WELL OF COURSE...WHILE THERE ARE JUST A FEW OF THEM, THEY ARE JUST FADDISH STATUS SYMBOLS, BUT IMAGINE HOW THAT WOULD CHANGE IF EVERY HOUSEHOLD HAD ONE...

YES...

THEY'D BECOME TOTALLY NAFF... JUST LIKE SATELLITE DISHES DID... I'M ALREADY THINKING OF GETTING RID OF OURS...

Alex PEATTIE + TAYLOR

DO YOU KNOW THERE'S A HEDGE FUND THAT RUNS ITS OWN FANTASY INVESTMENT LEAGUE. EVERY MONTH THE WINNER GETS A METHUSELAH OF CHAMPAGNE...

ALL THE ANALYSTS PLAY IT AND OF COURSE THE HEDGE FUND GETS THE BENEFIT OF ALL THEIR BEST IDEAS... BUT THAT MAKES A MOCKERY OF THE NOTION OF EQUALITY OF ACCESS TO INFORMATION...

I THOUGHT THE MODERN REGULATORY REGIME WAS ALL ABOUT TRANSPARENCY, FAIRNESS AND INTEGRITY. THIS IS A SAD REFLECTION OF WHAT THE FINANCIAL WORLD HAS COME TO. IT CERTAINLY IS.

I REMEMBER A TIME WHEN ANALYSTS COULD AFFORD THEIR OWN CHAMPAGNE. YES, WHEN WE BANKERS WERE ALLOWED TO BRIBE THEM WITH A CUT OF OUR BONUSES TO WRITE NICE THINGS ABOUT OUR CLIENTS...

Alex PEATTIE + TAYLOR

THIS NEW INSIDER'S COLUMN ABOUT THE FINANCIAL WORLD IS RATHER GOOD. I WONDER WHO WRITES IT...? AHEM... ACTUALLY, ALEX... IT'S ME...

YOU, CLIVE?! YOU ARE "CITYCHAP"? YES, BUT DON'T TELL ANYONE...IT'S GREAT... I GET TO WRITE ALL ABOUT MY HIGH-FLYING LIFE AS A TOP INVESTMENT BANKER...

AND OF COURSE, COMING ACROSS AS A RICH, SUCCESSFUL, POWERFUL MAN HAS A PREDICTABLE EFFECT ON THE LADIES... MY INBOX AT CITYCHAP.COM IS FULL OF E-MAILS FROM THEM... LIKE THIS ONE... LET'S HAVE A LOOK... AH, YES...

...ASKING YOU TO GET HER SON A SUMMER INTERNSHIP AT THE BANK... I WOULDN'T MIND IF THE OCCASIONAL ONE WANTED TO SLEEP WITH ME...

Alex PEATTIE + TAYLOR

YOU'VE MADE SOME PRETTY DAMNING REVELATIONS ABOUT LIFE AT OUR BANK IN YOUR SECRET NEWSPAPER COLUMN OF LATE, CLIVE.

YES... AND EVEN THOUGH I DON'T USE NAMES IT'S VERY CLEAR TO MANAGEMENT WHICH ORGANISATION IS BEING TALKED ABOUT. I UNDERSTAND THAT A MASSIVE INTERNAL WITCH HUNT HAS BEEN LAUNCHED TO UNEARTH THE MOLE... YES... I'VE HEARD THAT...

THEIR REACTION SAYS IT ALL, ALEX. THERE ARE CERTAIN UNCOMFORTABLE TRUTHS ABOUT BIG GLOBAL CORPORATIONS THAT THEY FIND VERY HARD TO ACCEPT...

SUCH AS THE FACT THAT THEY'RE ALL ESSENTIALLY EXACTLY THE SAME AS EACH OTHER? QUITE. THE FRENZIED WITCH HUNT IS GOING ON OVER AT CONTINENT BANK...

MEGABANK

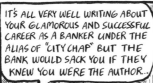

17

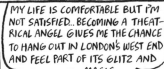

Panel 1: APPARENTLY THIS NEW PLAY IS A SATIRE ON THE FINANCIAL WORLD... / THEATRE BAR

Panel 2: WELL I SUPPOSE WE'RE FAIR GAME AT THE MOMENT, CLIVE, WITH BANKS ANNOUNCING BIG LOSSES AND CUT-BACKS AS A RESULT OF EXPOSURE TO SUB-PRIME LOANS...

Panel 3: STILL, NOT MANY INDUSTRIES WOULD TURN UP IN SUCH NUMBERS TO SEE THEMSELVES BEING PILLORIED... I THINK THIS REALLY SAYS SOMETHING ABOUT THE CITY... / YES...

Panel 4: ...THAT NO ONE'S GOT ANY DEALS ON ANY MORE... / EXACTLY... EVERYONE MANAGING TO GET TO THE WEST END BY 7.30...THIS IS FRANKLY EMBARRASSING...

Panel 1: HALLO! TAKING THE TRAIN TODAY, SIMON? DON'T YOU NORMALLY CYCLE INTO WORK? / ER... YES...

Panel 2: HA! TYPICAL. PEOPLE LIKE YOU MAKE SUCH A BIG SHOW OF ESPOUSING GREEN VALUES TO YOUR OFFICE DURING THE SUMMER MONTHS...

Panel 3: BUT ONCE THE AUTUMN SETS IN, SUDDENLY THE IDEA OF SPENDING 45 MINUTES ON YOUR BIKE TWICE A DAY DOESN'T SEEM SO ATTRACTIVE. / OF COURSE NOT, CLIVE...

Panel 4: I'VE GOT TO SHOW MY BOSS I'M REALLY BUSY AND CAN'T AFFORD TO WASTE ALL THAT VALUABLE BLACKBERRY TIME... / AH. OF COURSE. IT'S THE BONUS SEASON.

Panel 1: IT'S GOOD THAT THE POST OFFICE WORKERS HAVE CALLED OFF THEIR STRIKE AND MAIL IS BEING DELIVERED AGAIN... / AGREED, CLIVE...

Panel 2: IT COULD HAVE BEEN POTENTIALLY VERY DAMAGING... AFTER ALL THE GROWING USE OF THE INTERNET AND E-MAIL HAS AFFECTED THE DEMAND FOR OLD-FASHIONED PHYSICAL TRANSPORTATION OF POST...

Panel 3: AND IF PEOPLE WHOSE BUSINESS IT IS TO DELIVER MAIL ARE SITTING AROUND IDLY, RATHER THAN WORKING, IT CAN ONLY LEAD TO THEM LOSING THEIR JOBS IN THE LONG TERM... / I KNOW WHAT YOU'RE TALKING ABOUT...

Panel 4: THE BANK'S INTERNAL COURIERS. / QUITE. WE WOULDN'T WANT MANAGEMENT TO REALISE THAT THEIR ONLY FUNCTION THESE DAYS IS TO DELIVER OUR ON-LINE SHOPPING TO OUR DESKS... / AH. THANKS.

Panel 1: OCTOBER CLUB 20TH ANNIVERSARY / THE OCTOBER CLUB ANNUAL DINNER IS ONE OF THE PRIME CITY EVENTS FOR NET-WORKING AND PICKING UP INFORMATION AND GOSSIP...

Panel 2: TRUE, BUT IT'S ALSO A GENEROUS CHARITABLE FUND RAISER... / OF COURSE. OUR AUCTION LIST IS ALWAYS IMPRESSIVE, EVEN IN A YEAR LIKE THIS WHEN THERE HAVE BEEN PROBLEMS IN THE MARKETS...

Panel 3: THE AUCTION CATALOGUE IS THE FIRST PLACE THAT LONG-TERM ATTENDEES LIKE ALEX TURN. HE'S FAMILIAR WITH ALL THE REGULAR LOTS AND ALWAYS SEEKS OUT THE MOST PRESTIGIOUS AND LUXURIOUS ITEMS...

Panel 4: I SEE YOU HAVEN'T OFFERED THE USUAL WEEKEND ON YOUR YACHT IN ST TROPEZ THIS YEAR, PETER... WHAT HAPPENED? DID YOU HAVE TO SELL IT? / YES...WE'VE HEARD YOUR HEDGE FUND IS IN TROUBLE.

Alex PEATTIE + TAYLOR

ANOTHER GOOD THING ABOUT ALL OUR BONUSES BEING GUARANTEED THIS YEAR IS WE DON'T HAVE TO BOTHER LOBBYING OUR BOSSES...

TRADITIONALLY IN THE LAST QUARTER WE'LL FIND SOME SPURIOUS BUSINESS PRETEXT TO BE IN NEW YORK SO THAT WE CAN REMIND THE SENIOR DECISION-MAKERS AT HEAD OFFICE OF OUR EXISTENCE...

BUT THIS YEAR FOR ONCE WE WON'T HAVE TO GO TO ALL THE TROUBLE OF ARRANGING SOME TOTALLY GRATUITOUS BUSINESS TRIP OUT THERE JUST TO CURRY FAVOUR WITH THE PEOPLE WHO RULE OUR LIVES...

SPEAK FOR YOURSELF, ALEX...

I MEAN, YOU TRY TELLING BRIDGET THAT HER ANNUAL PRE-XMAS NEW YORK SHOPPING JAUNT HAS BEEN DEEMED SURPLUS TO REQUIREMENTS...

Alex PEATTIE + TAYLOR
THEATRE BAR

I HEAR THAT ALEX IS AN INVESTOR IN THIS PLAY?

WELL, THE THEATRICAL WORLD COULDN'T EXIST WITHOUT MONEY MEN LIKE HIM...

IT'S A SYMBIOTIC RELATIONSHIP. THE SHOW GETS ITS FINANCING AND ALEX IS ABLE TO ENTERTAIN HIS CLIENTS AT IT AND GAIN KUDOS IN THEIR EYES BY CASUALLY MENTIONING THAT HE'S ONE OF THE "ANGELS"...

SO AN EVENT LIKE THIS CAN ALLOW US CITY BANKERS TO FIND COMMON GROUND WITH PEOPLE WHOSE WORK IS DIAMETRICALLY OPPOSED TO THE BUSINESS OF MAKING MONEY AND DOING DEALS...

WHAT, ARTY CREATIVE TYPES?

ER, NO... COMPLIANCE OFFICERS LIKE TREVOR THERE...

ALEX, YOU MUST DISCLOSE THAT YOU HAVE A FINANCIAL INTEREST IN THIS VENTURE...

FOR ONCE IT WILL BE MY PLEASURE TO COMPLY, TREVOR...

Alex PEATTIE + TAYLOR

EARLIER THIS YEAR WHEN THE BANK WAS A TAKEOVER TARGET WE GUARANTEED EVERYONE'S BONUS AT THE SAME LEVEL AS LAST YEAR'S...

FRANKLY IT WAS A CALCULATED PLOY TO PREVENT KEY PERSONNEL FROM DEFECTING AND THUS KEEP UP THE BANK'S VALUE TO A POTENTIAL BUYER, BUT IT'S HAD A DISCERNABLE PSYCHOLOGICAL EFFECT ON STAFF...

AFTER ALL, EVERYONE NEEDS TO FEEL WANTED, APPRECIATED, LOVED, EVEN WHEN THEY KNOW ITS ONLY MOTIVATED BY CYNICAL FINANCIAL CONSIDERATIONS...

IT'S WEIRD. NORMALLY AT THIS TIME OF YEAR ALL THE GUYS WANT TO TAKE ME OUT FOR LUNCH, DRINKS OR DINNER...

WELL WITH BONUSES FIXED, NO ONE NEEDS TO BOTHER TO LOBBY YOU, CYRUS...

MILDLY PUT OUT

Alex PEATTIE + TAYLOR

ONE LAST QUESTION BEFORE I END THIS JOB INTERVIEW: WHAT'S THE NOTICE PERIOD ON YOUR CURRENT JOB?

ER... ONE MONTH...

SPLENDID... WELL, LOOK, AS FAR AS I'M CONCERNED THE JOB HERE AT MEGABANK IS YOURS... H.R. WILL SORT OUT THE DETAILS OF THE FORMAL OFFER...

GREAT! THANK YOU SO MUCH!

WELL, WHY WASTE ANY TIME? WE'RE ALL VERY EXCITED ABOUT YOU COMING ON BOARD. I ANTICIPATE YOU'RE GOING TO BE A VALUABLE MEMBER OF OUR TEAM...

WHEW! SO WE'VE GOT SOMEONE TO MAN THE DESK OVER XMAS AND NEW YEAR...

WELL, EVERYONE ELSE WAS REFUSING TO DO IT AND HE WON'T BE ELIGIBLE FOR ANY HOLIDAY...

INTERVIEW ROOM

25

Alex *PEATTIE + TAYLOR*

THIS SUB-PRIME DEBT CRISIS REMINDS ME OF THE BARINGS COLLAPSE A DECADE AGO...

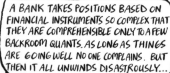

A BANK TAKES POSITIONS BASED ON FINANCIAL INSTRUMENTS SO COMPLEX THAT THEY ARE COMPREHENSIBLE ONLY TO A FEW BACKROOM QUANTS. AS LONG AS THINGS ARE GOING WELL NO ONE COMPLAINS. BUT THEN IT ALL UNWINDS DISASTROUSLY...

WELL, IN THIS CASE IT'S NOT JUST US WHO LOST MONEY, RUPERT... THE HERD MENTALITY TOOK OVER. ALL OUR COMPETITORS SAW WHAT WE WERE DOING AND DECIDED TO PILE IN TOO...

YES.

...AND POACHED ALL THE PEOPLE IN OUR ORGANISATION WHO ACTUALLY UNDERSTAND THESE BLASTED THINGS... NOW THERE'S NO-ONE LEFT HERE WHO HAS A CLUE WHAT OUR DOWNSIDE IS...

Alex *PEATTIE + TAYLOR*

YOU'RE A CITY BANKER, CLIVE, SO YOU MIGHT FEEL IT'S HARD TO FIND COMMON GROUND WITH A LAPDANCER LIKE ME...

BUT CAN I JUST SAY THAT ONE SHOULD NOT BE JUDGEMENTAL ABOUT HOW SOMEONE ELSE CHOOSES TO MAKE A LIVING... AFTER ALL THEY MAY NOT NECESSARILY BE PROUD OF WHAT THEY HAVE TO DO...

BUT IT'S EASY MONEY AND YOU TELL YOURSELF YOU'LL ONLY BE DOING IT FOR A SHORT TIME. BUT THEN YOU GET SUCKED INTO ITS WORLD, YOU BECOME DEPENDENT ON THE LIFESTYLE IT ALLOWS YOU TO AFFORD AND YOU CAN'T ESCAPE.

HMM... OKAY...

SO THAT'S THE CITY... NOW TELL ME ABOUT *YOUR* JOB...

SEE? WE HAVE MORE IN COMMON THAN YOU THINK...

Alex *PEATTIE + TAYLOR*

YES, LAPDANCING AND INVESTMENT BANKING ARE SIMILAR IN SOME WAYS BUT THEY ALSO HAVE THEIR DIFFERENCES...

LOOK AT *ME*. I'M 24 AND I'M EARNING GOOD MONEY WORKING HERE BUT HOW LONG'S THAT GOING TO LAST? A GIRL'S ONLY GOT 10 OR 15 YEARS IN THIS GAME BEFORE HER LOOKS START TO FADE...

YOU'RE A SUCCESSFUL MAN, CLIVE, BUT IMAGINE HOW IT WOULD FEEL TO BE IN A CAREER THAT WAS DESTINED IN ADVANCE TO FINISH WHEN YOU REACHED YOUR MID 30'S

I TAKE YOUR POINT...

I TOLD ALL MY FRIENDS THAT I'D BE RETIRING BY THE TIME I WAS 35... AND HERE I AM - TEN YEARS AFTER THAT AGE - STILL WORKING.... IT'S EMBARRASSING...

Alex *PEATTIE + TAYLOR*

YOU SEEM QUITE FASCINATED BY THE WORLD OF LAPDANCING, CLIVE...

WELL OF COURSE, FABERGÉ...

YOU'VE GOT TO REMEMBER THAT I SPEND MY DAYS IN THE STAID, ARTIFICIAL, CORPORATE ENVIRONMENT OF AN INTERNATIONAL INVESTMENT BANK...

FOR ME THERE'S AN EXOTICISM TO YOUR EXISTENCE. I GET A VICARIOUS SENSE OF EXCITEMENT, A CERTAIN FORBIDDEN THRILL FROM HEARING ALL THE DETAILS OF IT... GO ON, TELL ME MORE...

WELL, THE GIRLS HERE CAN GET SACKED FOR HAVING CELLULITE OR WRINKLES...

A WORKPLACE COMPLETELY DEVOID OF H.R. REQUIREMENTS OR DIVERSITY DIRECTIVES ....THAT'S SO WEIRD...

Strip 1:

Alex PEATTIE + TAYLOR

SO THE DANCERS HERE DON'T USE THEIR REAL NAMES?

NO OF COURSE NOT, CLIVE...

LOOK, LAPDANCING IS ALL ABOUT THE POWER OF THE IMAGINATION, CREATING A FANTASY: SOMETHING COMPLETELY REMOVED FROM THE DRAB REALITY OF OUR CUSTOMERS' LIVES...

IT'S ALL ABOUT THE CONTRAST BETWEEN ROUTINE EVERYDAY EXISTENCE AND AN EXOTIC WORLD OF GLAMOUR AND SEX.. BEING NAMED DIFFERENTLY HAS THE EFFECT OF TOTALLY ALTERING THE PERCEPTION CREATED..

YOU MEAN WHEN MY CREDIT CARD STATEMENT ARRIVES..?

EXACTLY... ALL THIS WILL BE BILLED AS "FOOD AND DRINK" AND MAKE IT LOOK AS IF YOU WERE AT A DULL CLIENT DINNER...

alex@alexcartoon.com

Strip 2:

Alex PEATTIE + TAYLOR

IT'S UNUSUAL TO SEE A WOMAN IN A LAP-DANCING BAR AS A CUSTOMER...

OH, SOME MALE BUSINESS COLLEAGUES BROUGHT ME ALONG...

BUT DON'T YOU FIND ALL THIS IDEO-LOGICALLY OFFENSIVE?

WELL, ON THE SURFACE IT'S ABOUT THE EXPLOITATION OF WOMEN, BUT ANY SENSIBLE PERSON CAN SEE HOW IT'S REALLY THE OTHER WAY ROUND...

I'M A BANKER – A PROFESSIONAL WOMAN – AND WHAT I SEE HERE IS A SITUATION WHERE A CAREER GIRL IS ABLE TO UTILISE HER FEMININITY TO MAKE MONEY... IT'S HOW YOU REACT TO IT AS A FEMALE THAT'S IMPORTANT...

SO I'M GOING TO PRETEND TO BE REALLY UPSET AND THEN SUE MY BANK FOR COMPEN-SATION... THIS COULD BE WORTH MILLIONS TO ME...

alex@alexcartoon.com

Strip 3:

Alex PEATTIE + TAYLOR

I DON'T KNOW WHY YOU DEFEND THE BANK BUYING EXPENSIVE MODERN ART... WHAT POSSIBLE RELATION DOES IT HAVE TO THE BUSINESS OF BANKING IN THE MODERN FINANCIAL WORLD...?

WE END UP IN POSSESSION OF SOMETHING NONE OF US ACTUALLY UNDERSTANDS OR HAS ANY IDEA OF WHETHER IT'S ANY GOOD... LET ALONE IF IT'S WORTH WHAT WE PAID FOR IT...

IT COULD BE COMPLETE RUBBISH FOR ALL WE KNOW... THE ONLY REASON WE BUY IT IS BECAUSE EVERYONE ELSE DOES...

AH... I SEE... IT'S EXACTLY THE SAME AS HOW WE DO BUSINESS, ISN'T IT?

WELL, JUDGING FROM OUR SUB-PRIME DEBT LIABILITIES, YES.

alex@alexcartoon.com

Strip 4:

Alex PEATTIE + TAYLOR

OH LOOK: A CHEQUE. THAT'S NICE... AFTER ALL THEY'RE SOMETHING OF A RARITY THESE DAYS.

I'M SURPRISED YOU APPROVE, ALEX...

I'D HAVE THOUGHT YOU'D FIND IT OUTDATED AND INCONVENIENT IN COMPARISON TO AN ELECTRONIC TRANSFER DIRECT INTO YOUR BANK ACCOUNT... YOU DO WORK IN THE MODERN FINANCIAL WORLD AFTER ALL...

TRUE, PENNY. BUT SOMETIMES AN OLD-FASHIONED CHEQUE CAN BE THE MOST PRACTICAL METHOD OF PAYMENT...

WHAT'S IT FOR ANYWAY?

SEE FOR YOURSELF..

OH... A RETURN ON THE INVESTMENT YOU MADE IN THAT THEATRE PLAY.

QUITE, AND BY NOT BOTHERING TO CASH IT I CAN SHOW THE PRODUCERS HOW LITTLE THE MONEY MEANS TO ME...

alex@alexcartoon.com

THE CURTAIN CAME DOWN ON Alex

AND HE WAS RESTING OVER CHRISTMAS

33

Strip 1:

IT LOOKS LIKE THE CREDIT CRISIS COULD USHER IN A WORLD-WIDE RECESSION. THAT CAN ONLY BE BAD FOR BUSINESS...

WELL, LET'S TRY TO LOOK ON THE POSITIVE SIDE, ALEX. BANKS ALSO MAKE MONEY FROM ADVISING COMPANIES AND THAT'S GOING TO BE PARTICULARLY SIGNIFICANT IN AN ECONOMIC DOWNTURN...

WE'RE TALKING ABOUT ORGANISATIONS THAT MAY NEED RESTRUCTURING, THEIR BUSINESS MODELS OVERHAULING, FAILED OPERATIONS CLOSING DOWN, COSTS CUTTING AND REDUNDANCIES IMPLEMENTED...

RIGHT...

WELL, THAT'S THE BANKS... SO HOW SERIOUSLY ARE OUR CLIENTS GOING TO TAKE ANY ADVICE COMING FROM US..?

NOT REMOTELY... ESPECIALLY AS IT WAS ALL OUR FAULT IN THE FIRST PLACE. IT'S ALL VERY DEPRESSING.

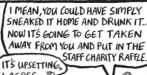

Strip 2:

I CAN'T BELIEVE YOU'RE INFORMING COMPLIANCE THAT YOU RECEIVED A CHRISTMAS PRESENT FROM A CLIENT. ESPECIALLY AS IT'S BOOZE...

I MEAN, YOU COULD HAVE SIMPLY SNEAKED IT HOME AND DRUNK IT... NOW IT'S GOING TO GET TAKEN AWAY FROM YOU AND PUT IN THE STAFF CHARITY RAFFLE...

IT'S UPSETTING, I AGREE, CLIVE...

BUT I HAVE MY REPUTATION IN THE CITY TO CONSIDER... IF I FAILED TO DISCLOSE SOMETHING LIKE THIS AND IT EVER CAME TO LIGHT, THE CONSEQUENCES FOR ME COULD BE SEVERE...

YOU MEAN DISCIPLINARY PROCEEDINGS?

NO, THE SHAME OF PEOPLE THINKING THAT I MIGHT NOT HAVE REALISED THAT A BOTTLE OF LAFITE ROTHSCHILD 2004 IS WORTH MORE THAN THE £50 AT WHICH GIFTS MUST BE DECLARED...

Strip 3:

ER... EXCUSE ME. CAN YOU KINDLY STOP CHECKING YOUR E-MAIL AND CONCENTRATE ON THE BUSINESS IN HAND?

EH?...OH, SORRY...

HMMPH!

AT ONE TIME BLACKBERRIES WERE ONLY FOR FRONT-OFFICE REVENUE-GENERATORS LIKE MYSELF, BUT THESE DAYS THE BANK SEEMS TO GIVE THEM TO ALL YOU MIDDLE-OFFICE BODS AS WELL.

HOLD ON!

MAY I REMIND YOU THAT MY DEPARTMENT IS VITAL TO THE RUNNING OF THE BANK, AND WITH THE CURRENT DIFFICULT MARKET CONDITIONS, WE HAVE A LOT OF WORK ON...

WELL PERHAPS WE COULD GET BACK TO IT...

FINE... ER, REMIND ME, WHERE WERE WE?

I THINK YOU WERE TELLING ME THAT I'M FIRED...

OH YES... THANKS...

BLASTED H.R. PEOPLE...

Strip 4:

I'M IMPRESSED THAT YOU WENT OVER TO SPEAK TO CYRUS IN PERSON, ALEX.

WHY'S THAT?

BECAUSE NORMALLY WHEN PEOPLE HAVE TO INFORM THEIR BOSS THAT THEY'VE LOST AN IMPORTANT PIECE OF CLIENT BUSINESS, LIKE YOU DID, THEY'D CHOOSE A LESS DIRECT WAY OF DELIVERING THE NEWS...

FOR EXAMPLE: E-MAIL IS SUCH A UBIQUITOUS MODE OF COMMUNICATION IN THE MODERN OFFICE... I'M SURPRISED YOU DIDN'T SEND HIM ONE OF THOSE...

OH, I DID...

WEIRD... ALEX JUST SPENT 2 MINUTES INQUIRING AFTER THE HEALTH OF MY FAMILY...

AN E-MAIL SCROLLS SO QUICKLY DOWN A BUSY EXECUTIVE'S SCREEN THESE DAYS THAT IT'S OFF THE BOTTOM AND OUT OF SIGHT WITHIN 90 SECONDS...

SHRUG

CYRUS HAD A WORKING CHRISTMAS

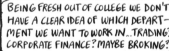

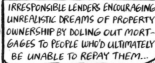

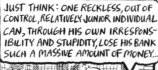

45

Alex (PEATTIE + TAYLOR)

WITH A RECESSION LIKELY IN THE WEST, EUROPEANS AND AMERICANS ARE FIGHTING FOR COMMERCIAL FOOTHOLDS HERE IN CHINA...

THIS POSES A PROBLEM FOR THE CHINESE, WHOSE ETIQUETTE PROHIBITS A SITUATION ARISING WHERE ONE HONOURED GUEST WOULD LOSE FACE...

THUS IN ALL DEALINGS WITH FOREIGNERS THEY TEND TO BE SCRUPULOUSLY EVEN-HANDED AND AVOID SHOWING PREFERENCE FOR ONE CULTURE OVER ANOTHER.

SO YOU RECKON THAT'S WHY THEY MIX LAFITE ROTHSCHILD WITH DIET COKE IN THE SAME GLASS?

ONE CAN ONLY IMAGINE SO, CLIVE...

=SHUDDER=

Alex (PEATTIE + TAYLOR)

ALL THE WESTERN DESIGNER BRANDS HAVE OUTLETS HERE IN CHINA THESE DAYS...

ORDINARY CHINESE PEOPLE ARE BEING ENCOURAGED TO HANKER AFTER EXPENSIVE LUXURY GOODS AS THEIR COUNTRY BECOMES JUST ANOTHER CAPITALIST CONSUMER SOCIETY...

GUCCI

IT'S SAD IN MANY WAYS, CLIVE... ESPECIALLY WHEN ONE CONSIDERS THE TRADITIONAL CRAFTS AND SKILLS FOR WHICH THIS PART OF THE WORLD IS KNOWN...

HERMES

WHAT, TURNING OUT FAKE DESIGNER PRODUCTS?

QUITE. SO EVEN IF PEOPLE HERE FORK OUT FOR THE *REAL* STUFF, EVERYONE WILL ASSUME IT'S JUST A CHEAP COPY...

LOUIS VUITTON

Alex (PEATTIE + TAYLOR)

I'VE BEEN TRYING TO CALL CLIVE BUT HIS PHONE GOES STRAIGHT TO VOICEMAIL...

SO WHERE IS HE?

HE'S GONE OUT TO VISIT A FACTORY IN THE COUNTRYSIDE...

AH. HE MAY NOT BE AWARE, BUT HERE IN CHINA THERE IS OFTEN NO MOBILE PHONE RECEPTION OUTSIDE THE CITIES...

OH DEAR... THIS DOESN'T BODE WELL FOR THE SUCCESS OF HIS TRIP...

CAN HE NOT MANAGE WITHOUT A TELEPHONE FOR A FEW HOURS?

YOU DON'T UNDERSTAND THE PRESSURES A MODERN INVESTMENT BANKER IS UNDER...

OH MY GOD! MY BLACKBERRY'S GONE DEAD... I MUST HAVE BEEN SACKED... HELP, HELP, HELP...

Alex (PEATTIE + TAYLOR)

WHAT I LIKE ABOUT CHINA IS THAT THEY DON'T HAVE THIS MISPLACED OBSESSION WITH YOUTH THAT EXISTS IN THE WEST...

BACK HOME PEOPLE OF OUR YEARS FEEL MARGINALISED BY THE NEW YOUNG BREED OF BANKERS AND THEIR VALUES, WHEREAS HERE THERE'S A TRADITION OF DEFERENCE TO AGE...

VERY TRUE, CLIVE...

CHINESE BUSINESS CULTURE SHOWS A REFRESHING OLD-FASHIONEDNESS AND IT'S ONLY NATURAL THAT PEOPLE OF OUR GENERATION SHOULD BE ACCORDED A SPECIAL RESPECT...

WELL, UNLIKE OUR JUNIORS, WE CAN HANDLE THE PRODIGIOUS ALCOHOL INTAKE REQUIRED OVER HERE...

QUITE... WITH LIVERS THAT HAVE BEEN SEASONED BY TWO DECADES OF LONG LUNCHES...

50

Panel 1: I HEAR YOU'VE BEEN GIVING SOME WORDS OF ADVICE TO CHRISTIAN, OUR JUNIOR, ON HOW TO COPE IN A RECESSION... WELL OF COURSE.

Panel 2: AFTER ALL, BEING UNDER 30, HE'S NEVER SEEN A BEAR MARKET BEFORE AND NATURALLY HE'S PANICKING... BUT THIS IS WHERE WE OLDER, EXPERIENCED PEOPLE HAVE A ROLE TO PLAY...

Panel 3: I JUST REMINDED HIM THAT I WAS ONLY ABOUT HIS AGE WHEN THE RECESSION OF THE EARLY 90'S HIT AND I MANAGED TO SURVIVE... THAT MUST BE OF COMFORT TO HIM...

Panel 4: THE BANK NEEDS TO FOCUS ON COSTS NOT REVENUE... RIGHT... WE WANT CHEAP LABOUR, REGARDLESS OF ABILITY... SO WE SACK ALL THE OLDER, EXPENSIVE PEOPLE? AGREED.

Panel 1: ALEX IS VERY PLEASED THAT THE CLOCKS FINALLY GO FORWARD THIS WEEKEND...

Panel 2: AS HE SAYS, IF THE AMERICANS CAN BRING IN THEIR SUMMER TIME IN EARLY MARCH THEN WHY CAN'T WE? THE CHANGE IN THE HOUR MAKES A BIG DIFFERENCE TO A BANKER'S DAILY ROUTINE...

Panel 3: BUT SURELY LOSING THAT HOUR OF DAYLIGHT IN THE MORNINGS IS BAD IF YOUR JOB REQUIRES YOU TO GET UP EARLY... ER...I'M NOT SURE THAT'S THE PART OF THE DAY HE HAD IN MIND...

Panel 4: SORRY, ALEX...GOT TO GET BACK TO THE OFFICE... THE U.S. MARKETS OPEN AT 1·30... ROLL ON NEXT WEEK WHEN THEY'RE BACK TO OPENING AT 2·30 OUR TIME AND WE CAN ENJOY A DECENT LUNCH AGAIN...

Panel 1: I'VE GOT TO PHONE A CLIENT TO CONGRATULATE HIM ON HIS LONDON MARATHON TIME AND HOPEFULLY GET SOME BUSINESS...

Panel 2: BUT I'VE JUST CHECKED THE MARATHON WEBSITE WHERE THE TIMES OF ALL THE 35,000 RUNNERS ARE LISTED... HE FINISHED IN WELL OVER SIX HOURS... WAY DOWN THE FIELD... OH DEAR... THAT'S NOT VERY GOOD...

Panel 3: NO, IT'S PRACTICALLY SNAIL-LIKE... A COMPLETELY RUBBISH PERFORMANCE THAT ANY HALFWAY DECENT ATHLETE WOULD BE ASHAMED OF... BUT YOU'VE GOT TO REMEMBER HE'S A CITY FUND MANAGER... THAT'S TRUE...

Panel 4: CONGRATULATIONS ON YOUR TIME... I MEAN 2,648 PEOPLE DID WORSE THAN YOU... COMPARATIVE PERFORMANCE IS ALL THAT'S IMPORTANT TO PEOPLE LIKE HIM...

Panel 1: HEY, I NEED YOU TO PHONE A CLIENT AND CONGRATULATE HIM ON HIS LONDON MARATHON PERFORMANCE... WHAT'S THE CATCH?

Panel 2: WELL, HIS TIME WAS USELESS...HE MADE THE TYPICAL NOVICE MARATHONER'S MISTAKE OF RUNNING THE BEGINNING OF THE RACE MUCH TOO FAST AND PAID FOR IT LATER ON...

Panel 3: HE HIT THE WALL AT MILE 10, HAD TO STOP FOR HALF AN HOUR AND THEN COMPLETED THE COURSE AT A WALK... AND I'VE GOT TO PHONE HIM? YES PLEASE...

Panel 4: I ESTIMATE THAT, MEASURED OVER THE FIRST SIX MILES, YOUR PERFORMANCE WAS IN THE TOP QUARTILE OF RUNNERS... YOU CAN ALWAYS RELY ON AN ANALYST TO SELECTIVELY INTERPRET THE DATA...

Alex PEATTIE + TAYLOR

SO, DO YOU FEEL FULFILLED AFTER RUNNING THE MARATHON, SIMON?

KNOWING THAT IT BENEFITED A CHARITY, YES...

OF COURSE IT COULD BE ARGUED THAT THERE'S SOMETHING INHERENTLY HYPOCRITICAL ABOUT PEOPLE WHO WORK IN THE CITY GETTING INVOLVED IN RAISING MONEY FOR CHARITABLE CAUSES...

BUT AS A FUND MANAGER IT MAKES ME FEEL GOOD THAT THERE'S ONE DAY IN THE YEAR WHEN I DO SOMETHING UNIQUE, SELFLESS, GENEROUS... NOBLE EVEN...

WHAT, ACTUALLY PICK UP THE PHONE TO THE BROKERS THAT CALL YOU?

WELL, THEY'VE ALL SPONSORED ME SO I NEED TO COLLECT THEIR PLEDGES... AND THEN LISTEN TO THEIR DUFF STOCK RECOMMENDATIONS

RING RING

Alex PEATTIE + TAYLOR

CORPORATE WIVES GET A BAD PRESS FOR BEING SHALLOW, MATERIALISTIC, MERCENARY AND SELF-INTERESTED

AND IT'S TRUE THAT IN THE GOOD YEARS THEY BLOW OUR MONEY ON TRYING TO OUTDO EACH OTHER ON HAVING THE BIGGEST HOUSE, THE FLASHEST HOLIDAYS AND SENDING THE KIDS TO THE MOST EXPENSIVE SCHOOLS...

BUT YOU'VE GOT TO CREDIT THEM WITH SOMETHING MORE THAN THAT... AND WHEN THE CITY SUDDENLY FALLS ON BAD TIMES, AT LEAST YOU KNOW THEY'RE GOING TO STICK BY YOU...

WE'D BE MAD TO GET DIVORCED _NOW_ AND HAVE OUR ALIMONY CALCULATED ON OUR HUSBANDS' _CURRENT_ NET WORTH.

QUITE. MOST OF THEIR MONEY IS IN THEIR BANK'S STOCK AND THE SHARE PRICE HAS _HALVED_...

Alex PEATTIE + TAYLOR

SO YOU'VE RECENTLY BEEN IN CHINA? HOW DID YOU FIND IT?

WELL, IT'S A COUNTRY OF FASCINATING CONTRASTS...

THOUGH THE STATE STILL EXERTS RIGID CONTROL IN SOME MATTERS SUCH AS THE ONE CHILD POLICY, IN OTHER AREAS THERE'S RELATIVELY UNFETTERED CAPITALISM...

IT'S A SYSTEM THAT HAS WORKED TO THE ADVANTAGE OF THE NEW AFFLUENT PROFESSIONAL CLASSES AND SEEMS TO MEET MANY OF THEIR NATURAL NEEDS...

SUCH AS...?

WELL, BOASTING ABOUT HOW MUCH YOUR CHILDREN COST YOU... OUT THERE YOU HAVE TO PAY A HEFTY FINE JUST FOR _HAVING_ MORE THAN ONE KID...

OUR SCHOOL FEES ARE £50K A YEAR... THAT'S NOTHING. OUR THREE BOYS SET US BACK OVER £75 K...

Alex PEATTIE + TAYLOR

THE CREDIT CRUNCH HAS BROUGHT A CERTAIN SATISFACTION TO OLD-STYLE CITY BANKERS LIKE US...

OUR TRADITIONAL APPROACH TO BUSINESS WAS PATRONISINGLY DUBBED "PLAIN VANILLA" BY THE HEDGE FUND WHIZZ KIDS, SO IT'S GOOD TO SEE THEM SCREW UP...

AND WITH BANKS HAVING WRITTEN DOWN HUGE SUB-PRIME LOSSES IT'S OPPORTUNE TO REMIND OUR BOSSES THAT _OUR_ WAY OF MAKING MONEY IS SUDDENLY BACK IN FASHION...

YOU WANT ME TO _INCREASE_ YOUR EXPENSE ACCOUNT, ALEX? BUT WE'RE CUTTING COSTS...

THE CORPORATE HOSPITALITY SEASON'S COMING UP, CYRUS... HOW ELSE DO YOU THINK WE PLAIN VANILLA BOYS BRING IN BUSINESS?

ALEX WENT SKIING
(WITHOUT CHRISTOPHER)

65

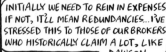

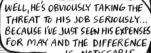

Strip 1:

THE BANK IS HAVING A TOUGH YEAR AND COSTS NEED TO BE CUT...

INITIALLY WE NEED TO REIN IN EXPENSES: IF NOT, IT'LL MEAN REDUNDANCIES... I'VE STRESSED THIS TO THOSE OF OUR BROKERS WHO HISTORICALLY CLAIM A LOT, LIKE DAWSON...

WELL, HE'S OBVIOUSLY TAKING THE THREAT TO HIS JOB SERIOUSLY... BECAUSE I'VE JUST SEEN HIS EXPENSES FOR MAY AND THE DIFFERENCE IS NOTICEABLE...

REALLY...?

YES, THEY'RE HIGHER THAN EVER... CLEARLY HE'S BEEN ENTERTAINING EVERY CLIENT HE'S GOT TO BRIBE THEM TO VOTE FOR HIM IN TODAY'S EXTEL SURVEY...

WELL, HE'D BETTER WIN OR HE'S DEFINITELY FIRED...

Strip 2:

BOWYERS CHARITY AUCTION

SO HOW ARE THINGS IN THE CITY? DO YOU THINK ANYONE HERE TONIGHT CAN AFFORD TO BID IN THE AUCTION?

WELL, OF LATE, EVERYONE'S BEEN IN A PANIC JUST TRYING TO WORK OUT THEIR COMPLEX SUB-PRIME POSITIONS, BUT THERE'S NOW A TENTATIVE FEELING THAT THE WORST OF THE CREDIT CRUNCH MAY BE OVER...

SO I'M CONFIDENT WE'LL SOON SEE A REVERSION TO STANDARD BUSINESS ACTIVITY FOLLOWING A PERIOD OF FINANCIAL CRISIS...

YOU MEAN THE BANKS WILL BE DOING DEALS AGAIN?

DON'T BE STUPID... NO CHANCE OF THAT... BUT THEY'LL ALL START LOOKING FOR SOMEONE ELSE TO BLAME AND SUING EACH OTHER...

SO TARGET THE LAWYERS ON TABLE SIX...

Strip 3:

RING

THE FIRE ALARM'S GOING OFF... WHO'S THE DEPARTMENTAL FIRE WARDEN?

IT IS ALEX, I THINK.

DON'T YOU REMEMBER? CYRUS MADE HIM FIRE WARDEN AS A PUNISHMENT...

WELL, WHERE IS HE? HE'S SUPPOSED TO BE IN CHARGE OF EVACUATING US...

I DO NOT KNOW, BUT HE CANNOT BE FAR AWAY.

HOW CAN YOU BE SO SURE?

LOOK, HIS JACKET IS STILL ON THE BACK OF HIS CHAIR.

OH GOD...

FIRE WARDEN

USING THE OLD "JACKET ON CHAIR" PLOY I MANAGED TO GET OUT OF THE BUILDING BEFORE THE STAMPEDE BEGAN.

ER... THE IDEA WAS TO BRING YOUR DEPARTMENT WITH YOU, ALEX...

MEGABANK

FIRE WARDEN

Strip 4:

I ALWAYS TAKE THE DAY OFF ON THE FOURTH OF JULY...

WELL, IT'S THE DAY WHEN YOU AMERICANS CAN WIND DOWN, CYRUS...

WIND DOWN? HELL, NO... IT'S THE ONLY CHANCE I GET TO CATCH UP ON MY BACKLOG OF E-MAILS... AND YOU'LL BE DOING THAT THIS YEAR...?

SURE...

WHAT?! YOU INTEND TO WORK ON AN OCCASION OF SUCH PRESTIGE AND SIGNIFICANCE, WITH ALL ITS HISTORICAL, CULTURAL AND SOCIAL RESONANCES...?

INDEPENDENCE DAY?

NO... THE MEN'S SEMIS AT WIMBLEDON.

OH THAT... YEAH, IT'S ALWAYS QUITE PEACEFUL IN THE HOSPITALITY TENT WHEN EVERYONE IS OUT WATCHING THE TENNIS...

WIMBLEDON INVITE JULY 4TH

68

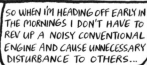

70

Panel 1: CYRUS, I'M HERE TO SEE YOU IN MY OFFICIAL CAPACITY OF DEPARTMENTAL SHOP STEWARD...

Panel 2: WITH INFLATIONARY PRESSURES THE COST OF LIVING HAS INCREASED CONSIDERABLY OF LATE AND MY MEMBERS ARE DEMANDING THAT THIS BE REFLECTED IN OUR SALARIES.

YOU GUYS WANT A RAISE, CLIVE?

Panel 3: WHY NOT? POPULAR PERCEPTION MAY BE THAT BANKERS ARE GROSSLY OVER-PAID, BUT IN FACT THE SALARY ELEMENT OF OUR COMPENSATION IS RELATIVELY MODEST...

WELL, I'M SURE THE BOARD WILL BE MOST INTERESTED IN YOUR REQUEST...

Panel 4: EXCELLENT. SO THERE WON'T BE ANY NEED TO MANAGE THEIR BONUS EXPECTATIONS THIS YEAR THEN?

WELL, IF THEY'RE WORRYING ABOUT THEIR BASIC SALARIES THEN THEY'RE OBVIOUSLY NOT RECKONING ON GETTING BONUSES AT ALL...

Panel 1: MANAGEMENT ALWAYS TRIES TO KEEP ITSELF BUSY IN A DOWNTURN...

YES. THE LATEST BUGBEAR IS INDUSTRIAL ESPIONAGE...

Panel 2: APPARENTLY SPIES HAVE BEEN TAKING JOBS AS CLEANERS IN BANKS IN ORDER TO SNOOP ON CONFIDENTIAL DOCUMENTS LEFT ON DESKS...

WHAT WILL THEY FIND? WE'VE GOT NO WORK ON..

SHRUG

Panel 3: I KNOW. IT'S RIDICULOUS. AND OF COURSE CLIVE'S WORKING ON A SATIRICAL NOVEL ABOUT THE CITY. TO HIM SOMETHING LIKE THIS IS AN ABSOLUTE GIFT...

Panel 4: WHAT? THE NEW "CLEAR DESK" POLICY?

QUITE... OBSESSIVE TIDYING IS A CLASSIC DISPLACEMENT ACTIVITY WHEN TRYING TO PUT OFF DOING ANY WRITING.

IMMACULATE

ADJUST

Panel 1: AS INVESTMENT BANKERS WE SHOULDN'T NEGLECT THE ECOLOGICALLY FRIENDLY LIFESTYLE CHOICES ONE CAN MAKE THESE DAYS.

Panel 2: FOR EXAMPLE, WE CAN HELP COMPANIES CUT DOWN ON THEIR USE OF PAPER AND THUS MAKE A SMALL BUT USEFUL CONTRIBUTION TO ENVIRONMENTAL PRESERVATION.

Panel 3: NOT FORGETTING THE BENEFICIAL EFFECT ON OUR CONSCIENCES AS WE WORRY LESS ABOUT THE POTENTIALLY HARMFUL CONSEQUENCES THAT MAY RESULT FROM OUR LIFESTYLES.

I KNOW WHAT YOU MEAN, CLIVE...

Panel 4: OUR AFTER-WORK SOCIAL ACTIVITIES?

QUITE. NOW THAT PRINTED BANK STATEMENTS ARE NO LONGER SENT TO OUR HOMES OUR WIVES ARE LESS LIKELY TO FIND OUT WHAT WE GET UP TO.

ON LINE BANKING

Panel 1: WELL, WE'RE ABOUT TO EXPERIENCE OUR THIRD RECESSION, CLIVE, AND SO ALL THIS LOOKS VERY FAMILIAR...

FTSE

Panel 2: BUSINESS LEVELS AT ZERO; COST-CUTTING RAMPANT; ONE'S FINANCES AND LIFESTYLE UNDER THREAT AS THE PROSPECT OF GETTING A BONUS RECEDES AND REDUNDANCY LOOMS LARGE...

Panel 3: IT'D BE EASY TO SIT AT OUR DESKS COMPLAINING AND FEELING DESPONDENT, BUT WE KNOW THAT IF ONE IS TO SURVIVE IN THIS ENVIRONMENT IT'S IMPORTANT TO BE PROACTIVE AND GET OUT THERE.

YES INDEED.

Panel 4: AS I ALWAYS SAY: AT TIMES LIKE THESE ONE HAS TO MAX OUT ON ONE'S EXPENSE ACCOUNT.

BEFORE THEY TAKE THAT AWAY FROM US TOO...

ALEX TOUR 2008

MELBOURNE 10th September
SYDNEY 19th - 21st September
HONG KONG 24th & 25th September
SINGAPORE 2nd & 3rd October
DUBAI 8th & 9th October
EASTBOURNE 21st October – 25th October
WINDSOR 27th October – 1st November
GUILDFORD 3rd November – 8th November
NORTHAMPTON 10th November – 15th November
COLCHESTER 17th November – 22nd November.
LONDON 25th November – 20th December

Also available from Masterley Publshing

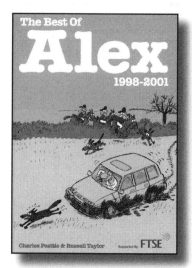

The Best of Alex 1998 - 2001
Boom to bust via the dotcom bubble.
£9.99 plus p+p

The Best of Alex 2002
Scandals rock the corporate world.
£9.99 plus p+p

The Best of Alex 2003
Alex gets made redundant.
£9.99 plus p+p

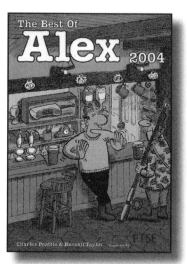

The Best of Alex 2004
And gets his job back.
£9.99 plus p+p

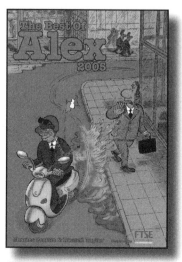

The Best of Alex 2005
Alex has problems with the French.
£9.99 plus p+p

The Best of Alex 2006
Alex gets a new American boss.
£9.99 plus p+p

The Best of Alex 2007
Alex restructures Christmas.
£9.99 plus p+p

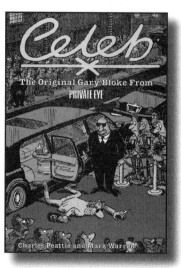

Celeb
Rock 'n Roll excess with Gary Bloke.
£9.99 plus p+p

Cartoon originals and prints
All our cartoon originals are for
sale. They measure 4 x 14 inches.
Prints are also available. All
originals and prints are signed by
the creators.

For further details on prices and
delivery charges for books,
cartoons or merchandise:
**Alex, PO Box 39447,
London N10 3WA
Tel: 020 8374 1225
Fax: 0871 750 2343
Email: alex@alexcartoon.com
Web: www.alexcartoon.com**